WHAT YOU BRING

R.G. ROBERTSON

www.roosterrepublicpress.com

PRAISE

"Media criticism can shape, frame or even re-create the experience of a story. As media rapidly metasizes into ever expanding mutations, the relationship between artist, fan, and critic evolves into some other kind of beast. RG Robertson has, with this work, created something personal, critical, and artistic, using different formats (essay, play, memoir, love story) to explore, in his unique voice, the relationship between head and heart, viewer and participant in the medium of film. He looks at film appreciation as an expression of the depth in personal relationships, an artistic and emotional short hand in how to better understand each other. He is breathing life into an often dead form, giving it a beating heart and head filled with his own memories. I want more."

--Laura Lee Bahr, novelist and director of 'Boned'

"Part personal essay, part meta-analysis, RG's writing on cinema is unlike any film criticism I've ever read. His discussion of Warrior reminds us why we love movies and why we love arguing about them. RG finds the sweet spot between film criticism and personal experience, and the result is entertaining and inspiring."

--Ezra Werb, co-author of *Cinescopes: What Your Favorite Movies Reveal About You*

WHAT YOU BRING

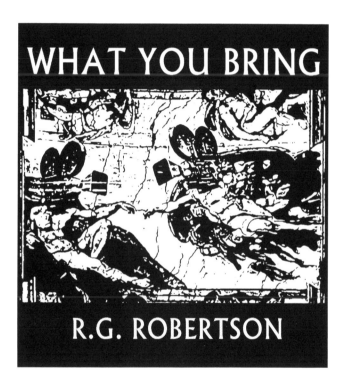

R.G. ROBERTSON

We expected something, something better than before
We expected something more

I like what I like, and I haven't seen all that I should have. I cannot engage in discussions of Troma or Bergmann. It would take me a long time to catch up on the prescribed list to allow me to assert that I am a cinephile; I'm not going to. The few folks I know who have earnestly taken the time to watch hours of sober, auteur-led, black and white affairs often make passing references to their readings and assume I take their meaning. I nod along.

I do like going to independent cinemas. I prop my head on my hand as I drink in the culture knowing it makes me a better person. I mingle beforehand in the foyer and buy a flat white in the quaint bar whilst I try to block out the accents of privilege, pontificating on various serious matters; they have found somewhere they can confidently stride about with their *ticket to the show* amongst like-minded and dressed individuals feeling completely at ease, oblivious to the shitstorm going on outside. I ham up my confused accent as I talk to my viewing partner and draw looks off those making the most convoluted attempts to manifest themselves as they feel they should.

Battered blue boat shoes paired with loose-fitting jogging bottoms is a favourite of mine, up top they've spent some time on their flop of hair and always pay in small change. Fuck right up, mate.

My viewing partner is now Emma. She loves receiving an academic essay on the film as we hand over our tickets to have them torn in order to confirm we've seen the filum. During the filum she has developed a Morse code of hand squeezes to note down a talking point. Afterwards she excitedly goes into detail about mise-en-scene, metaphorical meaning, and does a Leger Test to see how many relevant intertextual references she can bounce between. I love listening to her; she's usually correct and values my brutish input- I'm no' daft. During a screening of *Moonlight* I let out a shout of 'Yas!' as Chiron lifted the school chair to fuck his tormentor over the back. Emma laughed as she shooshed me quiet, reminding me afterwards that no one else felt the need to cry out in support of the protagonist.

She did her dissertation on the nihilism of Woody Allen films. Good craic. I've never asked her to explain it or let me read it. I did do some reading of my own in order to allude to it in episode six:

INT. CAFÉ VERONA ten minutes later.

Plates are cleared and they thank the WAITER.

                    RACHEL
          So give me a summary

of your thesis.

                    EMMA
        Oh...uch I don't want to
          bore you with that.

                   RACHEL
      Well, talking about 'stuff'
    is basically all that Mark does...
           (Smiles at MARK)
        ...I'm getting used to it
      and this fits that heading.

                    EMMA
      Well, I was actually reading
        an article on the subject
          recently and...well...
               (A beat)
      the world is awful, it's a
      shite situation to be in.
       So people make up stuff,
     things they tell themselves
     to survive: religion, fate,
         whatever the fuck.
    Ultimately it's all pointless.

                    MARK
    It's the bit from 'Annie Hall'
               int it?

             MARK and EMMA
       (As Alvy Singer's Mother)
        'He says the universe is
      expanding. Brooklyn isn't
              expanding.'

EMMA
Exactly! That's it!

MARK
I figured it out when I was
eight: fuck, I'm going to
die some day, and that's it!
So I thought, 'I'll
become famous and people
will remember' but then I
realised that the universe
ends anyway so what the fuck?

EMMA
That is exactly it.
Meaning is absurd.
So meaninglessness takes hold,
which in turn…
has its implications.

MARK
The universe is indifferent bud.

EMMA
Correct.

EMMA (CONT.)
(Towards RACHEL)
Your man has summed it
up perfectly.

RACHEL
So what's the implication?

                    EMMA
        Well, it's a perspective
        isn't it? Perhaps suggests
        an increased incidence of
        neurosis if understood.
                (Looks at MARK)
        But it doesn't necessarily
        mean you act any different.

                    MARK
        Just means nothing matters.

EMMA raises a finger.

                    EMMA
                 Correct!

                    MARK
                (As he rises)
        Crackin' Metallica song.

MARK goes to the bathroom.

                    RACHEL
           I think I get it, so
        that's why 'Whatever Works'?

She hasn't got to episode six yet but would
probably criticise me as clumsy in my attempt to
be concise.

I have tried watching Woody Allen. I like the
funny ones and he is undoubtedly insightful, but I
find the more serious films a bit of a chore. I
haven't told her this, it would break her heart.

Whatever Works is my favourite, which I know is a laughable choice. But Larry David does a comedic take on the night time death anxiety I experience and identifying with a character is not to be overrated. His night time funny turn leads him to go to the hospital but I never see the point in this; they can't change the *absolute* nature of the truth that inspires my turns so why stay up all night in A & E?

I open my eyes and start to scream 'No!' as I jump out of bed and find something to smash up. I tend to run out of steam after a couple of minutes and sit panting, embarrassed, hoping the neighbours didn't hear me- they always do.

When I stayed with Sasha our downstairs neighbour was an auld dear with dementia. On our first night staying in the new flat I was watching Jose Padilha's *Robocop;* there is a scene near the end of the film in which the Robocop suit is removed to reveal- for a second time- that all that is left of Alex Murphy is his head, heart, lungs and left hand. The existential dread accelerated from my unconscious to conscious mind and I jumped out of bed screaming. I paced the length of the hall twice still screaming as hard as I could before putting my foot through the partition wall and then re-entering the bedroom. Sasha tried to put her arms around me and speak in a soothing tone. I made makeshift lapels out of her t-shirt and shook her by them still screaming; it then started to dissipate. I lay down on the bedroom floor, embarrassed and upset that I had acted aggressively toward sweet Sasha.

I was out walking Charlie the next day when the neighbour's daughter stopped me in the street, concerned about her mother. The daughter was a nosey cunt, the kind of woman who would dismiss anyone who didn't hold her exact opinion on how to carry out your life, nae harm tae her. She asked if I had heard any screaming the previous night; her mother had reported my incident. What was I going to do, tell her it was me? Or tell her that, aye, I had heard some strange screaming? If I had done the former then she'd have had me down as a lunatic, and if I did the latter she would've probably approached the other neighbours to try to get to the bottom of it. So, and I still regret this, I told her I had heard nothing. She explained she was becoming increasingly concerned about her mother and that she would soon not be able to live herself. She did say that her mother had reported voices on other occasions which helped assuage the guilt.

I try to keep the terrors to myself.

*

I do have favourites, and folk usually nod along to acknowledge their validity. Emma's initial interest in me was greatly increased when I told her Blade Runner was in my top five filums. It is her absolute favourite, she watches it with a beautiful child-like fascination; I have to work hard to keep her quiet.

'The vistas; the depth of detail;' she gestures towards the screen with two fingers, twisting, focusing on little nuances, 'the way its world is assumed and not picked over; the way it clashes hard-boiled film noir with science-fiction...look! look! look!' she swoons, 'how handsome is he?

Aw man- Top Five, laminated. Look at him, says it all with the slightest smirk…amazing.'

And she loves the soundtrack. As she should, it is a crucial part of the immersive nature of the filum, both the music and the constant soundscape add to the sexy, dream-like, three-dimensional, nostalgic future world where the swirling cigarette smoke is now an odd anachronism.

She knows everything about the filum. She has read extensively about the production of the film in a way I have never bothered to with any filum. I tend to take things as they are presented to me: *there's yer artefact, what ye think?* But this does sometimes lead to Emma ripping me when I fail to comment on something obvious. Like the parallel structure in *Their Finest*. A shite film I have no interest in ever seeing again.

'How can you not see that the storylines they are devising are paralleled in their story, are you an idiot?'

Sometimes I take it to heart. And other times I think: fuck it, she had never heard of the term 'trope' till yer aul' da introduced her to it.

If I was to pick my favourite science-fiction filum it would be Duncan Jones' *Moon*. What a filum. It's simple, it has a clever conceit, a quality soundtrack and a single sublime, heart-breaking moment. The Clint Mansell soundtrack carries you through the exposition nodding to its forebears and building up a tension with a piercing string part. I was intrigued, and I don't often experience that with a filum.

I took the film to be exploring the mental breakdown of its only character, Sam. A psychosis caused by his isolation. I supposed that the second

Sam that Sam finds was due to him craving human interaction and read the filum that way. This reading afforded hope; my Sam would soon be on his way home to his wife and daughter and would be able to recover from the ordeal of being the only man stationed on a fuel mining moon station. I allowed myself to be swept along and didn't try to second guess the narrative.

See when cunts say 'I knew that was going to happen' it annoys me- *fuckin' good for you, ya clown*. There are shite films where it is abundantly clear what is happening but more often than not, with well vetted filums, there is enough ambiguity to allow the viewer to suspend their disbelief and go along. I beg of you, go along. There is so much to be enjoyed out there if you would just fuck up and enjoy the film for what it is rather than trying to constantly intellectualise it and show how clever you are. Because really, no cunt cares. No cunt cares if you are able to spot the fact that it draws on ideas from various other texts in its genre, surely that's partly what genre is? All that shite is for afterchat and subsequent viewings. The first viewing of a good film is an experience all on its own; allow yourself that pleasure.

Because, see that moment, that moment when Sam realises what is really going on...

So I watch it and I see a man who has taken a cunt of a three year shift working himself. I imagined it was like the das of boys I knew in school who used to go off to the rigs for weeks on end to then get weeks on end off at home. He struggles with the isolation and seems to be breaking down because of it. He has limited contact with home and watches pre-recorded video messages from his wife. He then takes a dunt on the head and starts seeing a younger version of himself walking about the station. The story could still go a number of ways.

Sam takes the other version of himself to be real and starts asking the space station's computer awkward questions. At this point I'm still not sure if the second Sam is real. Sam's neurosis continues to get worse and his physical health is also deteriorating. Sam argues with the other version of himself, with the second Sam suggesting that they are in fact clones. I eventually take second Sam to be a clone of Sam who is intent on getting to the bottom of it all. Sam, with the help and encouragement of second Sam- *paranoia*?- goes against company protocol- *good man*- to get to the bottom of everything and eventual manages to set up a live feed back to his home on Earth. Sam gets his daughter, Eve, on the other end of the line, she has jumped from being a baby to fifteen years old. Eve explains that 'his' wife has died and then calls on 'her' dad; Sam's voice, the voice of the *real* Sam is heard off-screen replying to Eve. In this moment our Sam accepts his reality. Sam now knows he is in fact a sentient clone who has been built to man the space station and will die there: there is no 'real' life for him, his existence is a lie. He has been burdened with hope that can never be fulfilled, a realisation which he was never meant to reach.

'That's enough, that's enough.'

Sam stops the feed, leans back, and in a profoundly futile gesture punches the interior of the moon buggy and then begins to gently sob saying 'I want to go home.' But there is no home.

I broke down. I was there with him. I could perfectly understand what he meant. It's a natural instinct but Sam wants to be the Sam who has that home, he only wants the reality he has been sold as real. We hear him sobbing and punching with the music intensifying and the camera pulling back to show Sam's moon buggy sitting, alone, on the surface of the moon. Sublime, existential isolation. Aloneness.

Anyone who is constantly suspicious of cinema, the kinda cunt who would play chess unsure of your next move but would 'ooh' and 'ahh' anyway, they'd've missed this sublime moment. And that's sad.

There were clues. Perhaps I was misreading, perhaps wilfully so, but it led to that sublime moment; I was right there with Sam. And that experience was so much more fulfilling than being able to tell some uninterested party that I had it all figured out by the twenty minute mark. Did ye, aye?

**

'God will forgive them. He'll forgive them and allow them into heaven. I can't live with that.'

I worked in a music shop for a couple of years. I thought that it would be just like *High Fidelity*. I thought that I'd be able to introduce beautiful shy girls to My Bloody Valentine and Pavement. Turns out that these shops are propped up by smelly men in leather jaikets looking for Motörhead albums and boring Scottish music enthusiasts enquiring about Capercaille's new album. Two years completely devoid of any nanny. I was beelin'. But we did get to listen to whatever the fuck we wanted.

Gavin used to recommend music to me. He had decent taste and wore his Slint t-shirt at least once a week, just in case that one beautiful, musically receptive girl came in the shop. It was usually a Thursday.

He got me into John Martyn and the Super Furry Animals. A good boy. He told me about his favourite singer, Smog, and ordered me 'Supper'. He suggested it was his best album- it's actually 'A River Ain't too Much to Love'.

So I took the album home and stuck it on. Nothing. Just this fulla singing in a baritone over sparse instrumentation. I listened through three times- I respected his opinion. Still nothing. Said nothing to me. I put it to one side and didn't bother too much since I was consuming a lot of albums at the time and you are always going to get a bum note. He did have a distinctive dead-pan delivery but I didn't get it.

So then one evening I found myself lying on the couch with Sasha in my arms looking for something to watch and settled on Film4's nine o'clock job. A Film4 production. British.

First couple of credits were at the bottom of a black screen with a simple guitar line playing. Then home video footage of little babies; the first one sleeping, then a second stirring. Then one of them in a loving relative's arms gently rocking the baby for the recording. Then relatives bobbing one of the babies, lovingly, up and down in a paddling pool. Then the christening, music continuing to build. Baby in its pram, rocked in the garden. A relative walking the baby with its feet on theirs. Absolute, sincere love. The love that hurts your face. The song lyrics have started.

I am just a vessel in vain.

The aged home footage gives way to a pastoral landscape with the land occupying the bottom three quarters of the screen and a blue sky filling the top quarter. After a couple of seconds this fades to more home footage. And I completely lost it.

The two babies are slightly bigger and the older brother rolls over to hug the younger one who smiles towards the camera. It's too much, I started sobbing with a smile. The older brother pulls the younger one towards him so he can hold him better, encouraging the younger one to cuddle him back. It's instinctive, not learned. I can feel the warm tears rolling. I smile and shake my head. It's me and Scot.

I mind when we were wee I was always cuddling Scot and he would push me away. Even as a tiny little baby he didn't like it. Then, when he could sit up himself, I would get him toys to play with, demonstrate how to play and kiss him on the head when he didn't understand. He didn't like this either. He looked a vulnerable little bundle, but even then, before conscious thought, he had other ideas. That's not to say he didn't love me. But I loved him from day one. No jealousy. He was a little fascination and I had no idea *why* I loved him. But I did. He was mine.

The pastoral part now has the two brothers walking along a farm road, the older brother strides with purpose whilst the younger brother awkwardly walks off to one side. That's not Scot.

The amateur footage continues with the toddlers interacting with besotted relatives and the cuts between home footage and recent pastoral gain pace along with the music. Christmas. Presents. The tree. Relatives drinking. Family.

Ideals on the run.

Family seaside breaks. Like I remember. Saltcoats. We used to go to a caravan in Troon and go to the shows at Saltcoats. We'd bounce on the trampolines and ride on the little circular butterfly cars whilst my mum looked on. We'd wave and she'd wave back. You smile and are incapable of thinking anything of it but those moments represent utter contentment for adults, parents, grandparents.

Free reign.

The opening sequence resolves with the older brothers walking towards a barn as the shot fades. I was broken. Four and a half minutes perfectly encapsulating my love for my brother. I was projecting but it was easy to do. And for those four and a half minutes alone I would be happy to call Shane Meadows my favourite director.

That song though. Bloody Smog. Cunt's a genius. I was embarrassed I hadn't seen it. It took *Dead Man's Shoes* for me to get it. He had pathos, that thing I most desire in anything I consume. I got it now.

I bought all the Smog albums and his more recent work as Bill Callahan. I imagine 'Vessel in Vain' played as my box is brought into the crematorium and I have 'Feather by Feather' down as one of Scot's funeral songs. He lives at a pace, I fear I'll have to bury the cunt and also have to break the news to my poor mother who will never get over it. *When they make the movie of your life...*

His pals cry him 'The Giant'. He has plenty. Ones who would do anything for him. They think he's mad because they can't compete with him; he will push things beyond anyone else just to prove he is willing.

I've been to visit him in hospital for four different accidents in the past year and each time I have met various dangerous fullas who are there by his bedside completely enamoured. These people would not give me the time of day were it not for the fact that Scot is my brother. But I can sit there knowing that even if Scot is in a hospital bed getting shite pumped out a wound in his broken leg he would jump out of bed and skull the cunt if they tried to start anyhin. And they know that anol.

I've been with Scot when one of these dangerous wans comes running across a car park shouting his name just to stand with him talking shite for a couple of minutes. They want to be around him, they see something they'll never have.

Unfortunately, I'm convinced they see a favour off him as a final resort, the nuclear option, no matter their game. Scot makes his money honestly but the dangerous ones know he is capable of outdoing anything they could come up with and they want him on their side just in case. I hope it never comes to that.

***

Visceral

About Today.

Cycling was always our sport. Our da was into it which meant we were indoctrinated. As weans we'd get traipsed out in odd, luminous, stretchy gear, and I hated it. My da would roll ahead of me for what seemed like hours and call back, 'It's just round the corner.' in the most sanguine tone he ever used. He was happy on his bike and could tolerate my greetin' because he had his boys out.

Scot loved it. He learned to ride his bike at the same time as me; I was four, and Scot had just turned two. He immediately learned to skid, the wheelies came later. He'd spend hours riding about the horrible little pedestrian lanes that surrounded our house, zipping in between aul grannies walking their messages home. He eventually wanted a victim so trained up his wee pal, got hold of my da's tools and took the stabilisers off Wee Pal's bike. Scot couldn't understand the tears or how ragin' the wee boy's mother was. My da thought it was hilarious, Scot was his *boy* from then on.

So the routine was repeated weekly. Scot would sleep in his bike gear the night before and be out early pumping up the tyres on his wee bike whilst my da tried to keep me happy by placing my helmet gently enough on my head as to allow my spikey hair to stick through the vents and maintain its integrity. This was often interrupted by a neighbour chapping the door to inform my da that

Scot had been up to mischief whilst waiting.

I mind the time he took us up the woods. Scot was too wee for a racing style bike so his was a mountain bike style affair, my da had similar.

I kept falling off. The tyres on my bike were too narrow and devoid of any grip. I'd make an attempt at a short, mucky run, the tyres would spin and I would cowp over. I'd try to ride canny down a short descent and the bike would completely wipe-out from underneath me. I'd have a go at a path of compacted dirt to be undone by some roots running diagonally across my path. Each time I'd end up on the sodden ground with a face full of muck. By the third fall I was mockit and wringin' wet. It was basically torture. The additional weight of my sodden clothes made it increasingly difficult to get up and I eventually burst into tears demoralised and aware that the torture was to continue.

Scot and my dad stood a way up the path each time I fell. They'd turn around and mock me.

'Come on, Professor Bumblebee.'

'Ha ha, aye, Professor Bumblebee!'

When I eventually cracked they stood and laughed. My da even took a photo; me, lying with the bike still between my legs looking toward the camera, helmet vents filled with dirt and my face screwed up like a Vietnamese wean looking for its parents after a good, aul' carpet bombing. My da did not pander, not even to an eight year old.

Scot still laughs the same way. If the notion takes him then he cannot control himself. He shrieks, either rocks back and forth or bounces up and down, and has to hold himself in case he pisses his drawers. My da just smiled and snittered slightly. After all, the prick still had to get his camera out.

Maybe I did need toughening up.

Cycling stopped us from engaging too much in the Bucky and bareback bam culture when we were the appropriate age. We'd dip in at intervals. Taster sessions. But it was few and far between. As it should be, I suppose. We managed to get through school without getting anyone pregnant. Because we were either out on our bikes or too tired from training to go out pummelling wee tidies.

We have both had periods committed to racing and periods away from it when, with the same appetite as when training, we'd both put on a power of weight. I mind I was getting back into it after I finished at university. I had been off the bike for four year and had put on two stone from the drinking. My head was still swimming from chucking the Regal King Size but I was on it. I had downloaded a calorie counting app, I was on the appetite suppressants you get when the bodybuilding shop locks the door behind you and I was gently building up my hours of training.

The first six months back on it are quality: the weight falls off and your endurance increases exponentially. But I knew I was a long way away from mixing with the racing boys, the year-in, year-out humourless, boring cunts who never eat dessert and go to bed early every night to try to get the jump on their rivals who, they suspect, are doing the same. They then turn up at their amateur event with their eight grand push bikes and get leathered into each other. These cunts are intense and I knew it would take me a good year back on the bike to be ready to involve myself.

Scot's attitude is different. When I said I wouldn't be going out with the training group until the following season Scot would bark, 'How?' in a confrontational tone, demonstrating his complete inability to understand my approach.

'Because I want to be able to spell through and go up the long way. It would set me back to get dropped.'

'You'll no' get dropped, it'll be fine, honestly. If you can get over the Bish hill then you'll be fine. Just go up the shortcut.'

He'd plead and plead, ragin' I wouldn't yield but I had to approach things my own way, methodically. Scot didn't need to do this. The cunt is an utter brute and within two weeks he'd be able to hand it out to the grey-gaunt racers.

He was pals with a young professional rider for a short period of time and the pro would use Scot to work on his top-end speed. This rider, for whom bike racing was his job, would be happy with his training if he could hang on to the burly joiner for half mile sprint intervals. I just have to shake my head, smile and get on with my year of graft.

I do get my victories though. Gravity is not Scot's friend. He's a big fulla and if I'm lean enough to race Scot is getting skelpt. With sprinting, bike handing and straight line speed Scot is unplayable under the right circumstance but the searing pain of lengthy climbs is such a big part of the sport that I can always take my doin' knowing my time will come.

So he appears at my work in his bike gear one afternoon when I was just getting back into it.

Scot had resolved he was going to race in a month's time and had decided bootin' my cunt in was the best way to kick start his training.

Principally, cycling and boxing are very similar. If you are to be good at either you have to make pain your friend. When one sees a fully committed racing cyclist flee by the immediate thought isn't pain, even cyclist spectators cannot imagine the pain empathically. Even racing cyclists forget about the pain when it's by wae. But when you are on the rivet it is all that exists. And it's the same pain for the Tour contender riding up the final alp and the desperado commuter trying to drop the cunt on the single speed. The pain fills your body, you can't quite get rid of the lactic poison quickly enough; everything else is neglected as your brain assists by diverting as much blood to your legs as it can and by informing you, 'Here, this isn't good for us, you've gone too far. Gonnae stop.' by firing up the pain receptors. Time slows down, you watch the seconds pass and consider free-wheeling. But you don't, you press on and know that next time it will either be easier or you'll go faster.

So we set off and I quickly figure out that he wants to drop me. He wants to go hard enough that I can't keep up. He rides two mile an hour too fast to be being sociable. I could try to trade blows with him, sharing the workload at the front, matching his pace. If I did this I'd be dropped in a few miles. I could always tell him to get tae fuck and turn off. I decide to sit in and see what happens.

I make myself small and focus on his back wheel. I can hear the constant buzz from his tyres and beyond that I tune out. We roll up and down the slight rises and dips in the road with Scot perfectly still on the bike. I sense the wind direction and move to his left and then right to gain the most shelter. He doesn't turn round to ask for a spell, he has accepted the terms I have offered and continues to roll along only moving from the hips down.

With every new stretch of road I wonder how long it'll be until I crack, until I continue to press the pedals as hard as I can but it's not enough, the stinging lactic acid causing my body to let me down. It's a wonderful thought, it has to come at some point and it'll be glorious. I'll free-wheel for a while and relax my neck, dropping my head whilst I take in long, soothing breaths.

He turns on to a six mile stretch of farm road I know well. It rolls, gaining height, then levels out before gaining more height and levelling out repeating this process a dozen times. The little kicks are never steep enough for the speed to drop right off. But I'm gassed, I'm hingin', I can taste blood. But I'll see it out, I'll do this until I physically can't do it anymore; that is the only acceptable time to stop. Stop before that and you are weak. Stop before that and you are an embarrassment. Stop before that and you shouldn't own a bike.

Then, on the final drag, before we'd turn left to descend, Scot got out the saddle. I couldn't believe it. He was struggling. He started using his weight to help him press left then right. He pedalled squares for a hundred yards at which point I was satisfied he was past the point of no return. I gave it the one and only burst I had. As I past him I could see the pain etched all over his screwed up face, sweat pishin' off him, each breath unable to help him square himself up. I pressed as hard as I could for as long as I could then looked back to see Scot struggling to keep the bike upright.

Given the right circumstance, guile can beat brute force.

****

I love showing folk filums they haven't seen. I enjoy subtly watching their face at a crucial moment or have them tell me how amazing my selection was. I currently have three filums I want to show Emma. She goes on about all yer various must-mention films but I try to keep my lists more focused. Filums I love and know others will too. Nothing too portentous, just good filums. The current list is: John Hillcoat's *The Proposition*; Carlos Sorin's *Bombon: El Perro* and Michael Winterbottom's *24 Hour Party People.* She enjoyed all my previous recommendations: John Carney's *Sing Street*; Taika Waititi's *Hunt for the Wilderpeople;* Shane Meadow's *A Room For Romeo Brass;* Paul Fegan's *Where You're Meant To Be* and Lenny Abrahamson's *Frank.* Maybe she's done better: Woody Allen's *Hannah and Her Sisters*; Woody Allen's *Crimes and Misdemeanours*; Woody Allen's *Vicky Christina Barcelona*; Ted Demme's *Beautiful Girls* and the Paul Feig television series *Freaks & Geeks.* Little tokens of distinction. Little offerings of personality. You are telling someone you have taste. If you pick a shite filum you are judged, if you go too earnest you are judged.

-'Naw, I've never seen *Battle Potemkin* or *Nanook of the North* and I feel the moment might've passed...'

-'Naw, I've never seen *The Hangover*, somehow I missed it...'

But you also say, 'You'll love this!' which is to suggest you think you know that person, that you have common ground; if it turns out they didn't like your recommendation then you have demonstrated that, at least, you don't know them and, at worst, they think less of you. Tightrope.

Scot hasn't seen many filums. Television, reading, filums, none of it is his thing. Fair enough. He could never sit long enough to watch a full film when he was younger. My poor maw tried her best. After the first couple of unsuccessful attempts she cracked it with *Toy Story*. She had the ingenious idea to neither buy anything before the start of the film nor take Scot to the bathroom. This meant she had a number of trips out of the auditorium with which to break up the eighty-one minutes. Poor wuman.

I have managed to get him to watch filums as an adult. But there has to be a hook. Under my watch he has sat through: Clio Barnard's *The Selfish Giant;* Derek Cianfrance's *The Place Beyond the Pines;* Asif Kapadia's *Senna* and Nicolas Winding Refn's *Bronson*.

The Selfish Giant. I told him the wee boys would remind him of his school experience: swearing at teachers, fighting in the playground and getting sent home.

The Place Beyond the Pines. A stunt motorcyclists starts robbing banks to give money to the mother of his wean. Scot enjoyed it but criticised the continuity when he could hear the protagonist's motorbike change from a two stroke to a four stroke engine in a single scene.

Senna. It was about motorsport but I was calling it my favourite documentary, he found this intriguing. He sat in awe of Ayrton Senna's abilities but was disappointed by his Faith.

Bronson. Britain's most notorious criminal battering fuck outta polis and prison wardens. A film which can be read as sympathetic toward its transgressive lead; Scot was on board.

I knew if I caught him in the right mood he'd love *Warrior.*

I didn't see it in the cinema, I had no interest in the film when I saw the posters and heard it described. As soon as I heard it involved mixed martial arts I was out. Then I caught a short clip of the trailer which seemed to include a massive spoiler. The mixed martial arts commentator reveals:

'This is impossible. The two men fighting for the championship tonight are brothers!'

Are they aye?

In the trailer there's glamour, there's machismo and there's all four main characters looking like they can't act worth a fuck. The music, that's what does it. The music is shite. Really terrible. They want to quickly establish dramatic tension through the music in the first section and do the same but to connote glorious resolution in the concluding part. Please watch it. But only after you've watched the filum. The music gives it this afternoon television movie gloss that bears absolutely no relation to the actual film- the film's use of non-diegetic sound being relatively sparse. Then there is a clip of the da punching the air shouting *'You got him!'* like an over-excited school girl, which doesn't fit with the tenor of the filum at all. Who the fuck made this trailer?

I decided this was a filum for the wans who walk about wearing sleeveless Tapout hoodies, the wans who get a wee tingle when they watch UFC, the wans who know aw the fighters' names. A straight to DVD filum with a demographic. If that was the case then fine, no issue. But it wasn't.

A third party, Big Al, whose opinion I respected, gave me the DVD and told me to watch it.

'It involves that new boxing stuff...' with a surprised snitter, 'it's pretty good.' So I went along.

It starts gently with establishing daytime shots of Pittsburgh: a slow freight train crossing the Ohio River; industrial factories puffing fumes and blowing whistles and residential streets with an old man saying his goodbyes outside a church. Two guitars play a slow, reflective tune before The National's Matt Berninger solemnly suggests that there is no walking away from this fight.

No aggression, just an honest, resigned warning. The old man then makes his way to his car, in which rosaries hang around the rear view mirror. His audiobook restarts as he draws away:

(Enter Ahab: Then, all)

It was not a great while after the affair of the pipe, that one morning shortly after breakfast, Ahab, as was his wont, ascended the cabin-

gangway to the deck.

The old man, Paddy, finds his son, Tommy, waiting for him when he arrives home. Tommy sits on Paddy's stoop drinking, ready. As Paddy draws up his audiobook ends on:

"It's a white whale, I say," resumed Ahab, as he threw down the topmaul: "a white whale. Skin your eyes for him, men; look sharp for white water; if ye see but a bubble, sing out."

There is a searing rage evident from the first shot of Tom Hardy, one he is unwilling to share or elaborate on. Nick Nolte's Paddy is vulnerable right from the start, he is trying to engage and reason with what seems to be a feral creature whose anger could erupt at any time.

Tommy is back after leaving with his mother as a teenager before spending time in the Marines. Tommy alludes to a history of domestic abuse and we sympathise with his quiet fury. Tommy looks at old family photos, reveals details about his mother's death and mocks the hypocrisy of his father's new found interest in God. Tommy's resentment, rage and grief are all beautifully rendered in Hardy's close-ups. The way he shifts his face, the way he works the bitter memories in his mouth, the way his body motions forward to provoke but then reels back to expose his own vulnerability tells you all you need to know. A broken masculinity. The scene ends with Tommy suggesting *'I think I preferred you better as a drunk.'* before falling asleep drunk with Paddy sobbing into his hands.

Enter domestic bliss. Out the backdoor of his beautiful suburban home brother Brendan- Joel Edgerton- is done up as a princess ably painted by his two daughters during a birthday celebration for one of them. Brendan and wife Tess smile and conceal whilst their excited daughter tends to her presents. Cut to their garage where they both discuss their evening jobs and Brendan's career as a teacher; they flirt, they seem happy, content.

Tommy then tentatively enters and joins the local boxing gym. This is juxtaposed with Brendan who is conducting a physics lesson to a fairly attentive class- lessons are always poorly portrayed in film, lacking pedagogical vigour, they always seem to have exposition close to the bell, never leaving enough time for a plenary or exit passes. In his lesson Brendan explains Newton's third law of motion: '...*for every action there is an equal and opposite reaction...thus setting the world back in proper balance.*'

This alludes both to Brendan's intelligent fighting style and to Tommy's unchecked aggression. Brendan often needs to use his opponent's momentum to his own advantage, he has a take a pounding, he has to accept he is going to get hurt and allow his opponent to punch himself out before landing that decisive blow of his own. Tommy, on the other hand, goes from the gun. Tommy is a classic big hitting, brutal pugilist whose approach is down to his ability to overwhelm his opponent. But we love that shit.

Our unassuming Tommy works a bag on the gym floor whilst some contender, Mad Dog, arrogantly knocks his sparring partner spark out. Tommy doesn't like Mad Dog's strutting and offers to '...*keep him warm.*' as his next sparring partner. Tommy doesn't suggest he is quoted, he doesn't strut, he just makes the offer waiting for his ability in the ring to do the talking. Mad Dog further goads Tommy before his offer is accepted. All Tommy's fury burst forth as he pummels fuck out of the arrogant cunt in a beautifully choreographed fight. Tommy wears an expression of absolute rage as he punches his opponents head from behind. Eventually three knees to the face and a right hook dispatches his quarry, no one is amused and Mad Dog's coach struggles to hold Tommy's gaze for longer than a couple of seconds. The fight was recorded on a camera phone and will soon be a viral sensation.

Meanwhile Brendan has to deal with Noah Emmerich's arrogant bank manager who could not give one solitary fuck for Brendan's financial situation: on advice of the bank he re-mortgaged and now it has become unfeasible for him to pay. The bank manager gets Brendan's job title wrong and guesses his daughter's long-term illness incorrectly. The only aggression Brendan demonstrates in this scene is passive when he asserts that: *'You've already told me that, three times.'* Taken together this is the more brutal scene.

We then see Paddy watching old tapes of Tommy fighting as an unbeaten teen wrestler before Mad Dog's promoter interrupts Paddy's dinner in order to ask for Tommy. Next up is Brendan's first fight scene in which he has to graft against street brawlers in order to make some money to help pay off his mortgage. Tommy then meets his da in a diner in order to ask Paddy to train him; he rejects having any sort of relationship with his da beyond training but Paddy is right on board, the fighter-trainer relationship suits them both.

I'm unsure exactly when I first cracked a light and started projecting but I was on board from the start, I found nothing to dislike. The brothers are set to eventually clash yet we sympathise with both of them, helping to maintain engagement with the narrative. But further to that, I had Scot cast as the show-stopping Tommy and myself cast as the journeyman Brendan.

My previous brothers sport filum was *Raging Bull* but the roles weren't easily devisable; neither Scot nor I, to my knowledge, has ever 'fucked' the others' partner so I could never decide who was Jake and who was Joey. The tension between the brothers in *Warrior* requires an underlying love and desire for reconciliation, *Raging Bull* not so much.

So I continued to watch the brothers' paths converge wondering if I'd be able to somehow overcome Scot's fury and force. Brendan is suspended from teaching because the school find out he is cock-fighting in lap-dancing club car parks. He starts training with his old coach and eventually gets a break in order to be entered in a winner-takes-all grand prix tournament, Sparta. Tommy gets his place in the same tournament for obvious reasons- the now viral leathering he gave the contender fella. Brendan's motivation is plain whereas Tommy's is revealed gradually as individuals tangentially connected to him help to piece his story together. Whilst they do this Tommy trains with his estranged da but has absolutely no interest in resolution; this gives Nolte his opportunity to continue the displays of broken masculinity when he finally breaks his sobriety- this scene being the first of two occasions when I cry during every viewing of this film; the second being when the final scene of the filum, the climactic fight between Brendan and Tommy.

I was invested in the climax, I was unsure who would win and for a sports film that's a fair achievement. By this point Tommy's past has been revealed to the public including his relationship to Brendan; all the incidental detail is squared up prior to the brothers' scrap. Brendan walks to the ring with a look of resigned conviction whilst Tommy seethes in his dressing room. The shots cut between the serious, contemplative looks of the brothers and the excited audience. The public cheer the enigmatic Marine vet character whilst the teacher is supported by the pupils from his school who watch at a drive-in cinema. Pulsing drums carry us into the ring.

Tommy knocked out all of his previous opponents with his first attack: that is not the case with Brendan. If one is invested then you can suggest that he wants to punish his brother rather than just lay him spark out. Or perhaps he is unwilling to land the decisive blow; or, if one considers the intensity required to knock out an opponent then it's fair to conclude that four in a weekend might be asking too much. These were the things I was thinking. I wasn't suggesting, in a nasal tone whilst shoving my glasses back up my face: *well, it would be rather anti-climactic if they didn't provide a pay-off, an immediate knock out would be a wholly unsatisfying ending.* No, instead I was rolling with Brendan as he took his beatin' and tried to quell his brother's apoplexy. Brendan fails to land a punch in the first round as his brother throws him around and cracks him a topper after the buzzer sounds. When they break, Tommy's rage is still etched in his every movement whilst Brendan tries to recover.

The beating continues in the second round with Brendan at least now attempting to throw back. The round ends with Tommy on top pummelling Brendan as if for fun. The referee needs to pull Tommy, who by this point looks like a rabid animal, off his brother; Tommy looking like he wants to destroy Brendan.

In round three Tommy again lays into Brendan with complete disregard for any move Brendan attempts. At first Tommy shakes the holds but eventually Brendan finds a chink to exploit and pins Tommy to the floor with his weight on Tommy's shoulder. Tess makes a tapping gesture in the crowd but Brendan knows he has to go further. A single, sickening crack sounds as Brendan breaks Tommy's shoulder. The buzzer sounds.

Brendan panics and looks to help his brother whose rage will still not subside. At this point Tommy looks around the stadium: he has nobody, he is a caged, cornered animal who will not accept defeat. Brendan tries to reason with him but it will not take, he softens Tommy up, stands back to look at his brother then, seeing that it still isn't enough, lays into the broken shoulder before the buzzer.

The National's *About Today* begins to play as they both retreat, exhausted. Brendan spots his father in the crowd who stands with the years of regret evident in his face. Tommy faces his corner and sobs, he is shot through the cage fencing with a harsh spot light shining over his shoulder, he heaves, he is trapped, a man entirely alone. The solemn strings tell us this is no triumph: there is nothing and no one to get behind.

They recommence for the final round: Tommy raising his one good fist and dragging his dud arm; Brendan stands square, looking at Tommy before lifting his fists. Tommy swings a couple pathetic punches whilst Brendan looks at him, seeing his brother beneath the fury. Brendan drops his hands and shakes his head at Tommy before throwing him a little faked move left to line up a kick to the face. The strings have faded as a more hopeful guitar motif begins. By this point I am always sobbing, enjoying the warm tears rolling down my face thinking about the lengths I would go to with my own brother.

Brendan now has his arms around Tommy's neck. Finally Tommy has to listen, finally he is exposed. Brendan delivers a line that looks trite but in the context of two exhausted fighters is entirely convincing:

> *'I'm sorry Tommy, I'm sorry.'*

About today?

> *'Tap Tommy. It's ok, it's ok.'*

How close am I

> *'I love you, I love you Tommy.'*

To losing you?

As Tommy yields, finally tapping Brendan's shoulder, I burst. Every time.

The guitar part becomes raucous and two violin parts become involved as the song reaches a crescendo. My first thought was that I had to show Scot. It wouldn't be the next day or week, I'd have to drop little previews into conversation and draw the favourable comparisons between him and Tom Hardy's character in order to get him on board- 'Mind the guy from *Bronson*?'

It was the week before Christmas. A Friday night. Scot appeared at mine and Sasha's flat with two bottles of Buckfast intending to stay. By this time Sasha had had to endure the filum a half dozen times; she'd always joke that it was ok because Tom Hardy was half-naked throughout- slightly less naked than in *Bronson*. She did like it, a number of occasions I heard her recommended it to others.

Scot and I had got through the neck of our bottles before I put it on. I think the viewing of *Warrior* is only improved by the consumption of caffeinated wine, you roll with each blow, moving back and forth imagining you know what you are doing.

I described the two brothers to Scot with him taking the comparison as a compliment. He looked at me with his mouth slightly agape, his expression eventually settling on intrigue whilst I tried to keep a lid on my excitement. Despite our differences I am always willing to admit to him how much of an affect texts have on me.

We settled down to watch with Scot lying on the floor and Sasha pressing her jean-filling thigh against mine. She was drinking cheap red wine from a glass and watching me enjoy showing the filum to my brother. I placed my hand on her thigh, gently squeezing every time a blow landed. We shouted at the tele during Tommy's first fight scene.

'Fuckin' yas!' Scot motioned a supportive heeder toward the screen.

I nodded, 'Know what ah mean!?'

Scot moved to a more engaged upright position as Sasha simultaneously smiled, rolled her eyes and shook her head. Scot had identified with the brooding Tommy and cracked a light as soon as he saw my proxy in the classroom.

'Ha ha ha! Ya beardy dick!' Scot jabbed.

'Fuck up ya cunt, ye see his wife? She's tidy.' He smiled as I tried to limit my defence, 'Tellin' ye, it's no' all about laying cunts out, ye need strategy...approach.'

We drained our bottles in solidarity.

Scot liked Tommy's da no' giving anything away to the fight promoter, he bought into the cards-close-to-the chest masculinity. He didn't say anything, I read this from the slightest wry smile.

The last scene I can remember before I fell asleep was Brendan's training montage. Buckfast is a beautiful drink which, unfortunately, has its associations with bam culture. In fact, Buckfast is entirely a bam signifier. One is not allowed to enjoy it in polite society unless one does so in a hip bar indulging ironically, possibly alluding to a working-class upbringing. Beyond that it is bad form. Scot's appearance with bottles had become a regular occurrence, a bonding ritual, a way for him to throw an arm around me and feel less alienated from his brother who now wears a tie to work.

I woke up to Sasha shaking me, asking me to come to bed. Once I remembered what had happened I looked for Scot. He was lying face first on the floor sleeping. The filum had finished but I had no idea how much of it he had seen. His bottle contained the same amount of wine as mine. I got up, turned the tele off and went to bed.

In the morning Scot sat on my feet at the end of the bed.

'You enjoy the filum?'

He looked away, '…Aye, it was awright.'

*****

Cerebral

'Ahab, you Godless son of a bitch, you stop this ship!'

'We're lost, we are all lost Tommy, we'll never make it, we'll never make it back.'

I bought into the film to the extent that I started to work on possible academic readings. My own personal taste dictates that Marxist analysis is always the priority: if I can perform a favourable Marxist reading then I can justify my own enjoyment of the film. These readings always start with Louis Althusser, not Michel Foucault. I watched the film again with this in mind looking for examples of interpellation, reciprocal action and state apparatus performing their roles. It's there.

In a filum which has pugilism as part of its central conceit it could be suggested that state violence serves a more crucial role as the motivator for our two protagonists. Indeed, the juxtaposition of Tommy's first fight scene with Brendan's bank interview makes this explicit:

Tommy is able to quickly achieve a sense of resolution within the scene, knocking out the antagonising, Mad Dog whilst Brendan has to sit and attempt to reason and plead with an unsympathetic bank manager; the contrast of Tommy's will to power and Brendan's helplessness nods to the sheer insignificance of individual triumph.

Brendan predominately interacts with *Ideological State Apparatus (ISA)* whilst Tommy's story is rooted by interactions with *Repressive State Apparatus (RSA)*. Brendan can't escape state institutions: he defends his *family* from the tyranny of the *banks* whilst trying to maintain employment within the *education system*. He is fighting to hold on to his *private property* for his *nuclear family*, a motivation which seems inherently wholesome to anyone watching; we internalise this and root for him to 'win'. It all seems so reasonable. Indeed, even Brendan's fighting style fits: he takes his beating and waits for his chance; things might be bleak but if one rolls with it long enough then an opportunity must present itself; but you have to allow yourself to take the beating, to not question it but instead aspire and have faith in the system. As the commentator calls him, Brendan, '…the civilian…' is constantly demonstrating *ideological recognition,* he is a perfectly interpellated concrete subject who strives to maintain both his own settled life and, in doing so, the conditions of production.

In the opening scene Tommy details how he joined the marines after his mother died a needlessly painful death unable to pay for healthcare; his mother's financial difficulties caused by fleeing the domestic abuse of the alcoholic Paddy. With the family *ISA* having failed Tommy, he moves toward the military RSA which our man Althusser explains '…intervenes directly as a supplementary repressive force in the last instance…'

The film gently suggests the possibility of post-traumatic stress disorder as the cause of Paddy's alcoholism and domestic violence. There is a deleted scene in which Paddy tries to discuss their time in the armed forces with Tommy who remains absolutely unwilling to talk about his experiences. The unspoken, broken masculinity of the film is perhaps not tied well enough to this narrative thread with its relevance never once referred to directly. But there is a neat cycle of violence and interaction with *RSA* that exists between Paddy and Tommy, with Tommy's service directly attributable to Paddy's post-service behaviour.

Tommy explicitly rejects the family ISA in his first scene with Brendan. They meet on the Atlantic City shore with Brendan looking for reconciliation. Both brothers stand open maintaining their own calm aggression. Whilst Tom Hardy beautifully portrays a man coiled, ready to react to one misplaced word, Joel Edgerton's performance comes with complexity: is he in fact afraid, is he maintaining an aggression that is premised on Tommy's inaction? This little note stood out as I often have this problem if ever discussions with my brother become heated; my aggression, a raised voice or a motion forward is always nothing more than bravado.

Brendan tries to show Tommy pictures of his daughters- Tommy's nieces- to explain why he didn't leave with Tommy and their mother.

'Why am I looking at pictures of people I don't know?'

'Because they are my family.'

'And who are you exactly?'

Brendan, astonished, *'I'm your brother, man.'*

'You in the Corps?'

'What?'

'I said, I didn't know you were in the Corps.'

'I wasn't in the Corps.'

'Then you ain't no brother to me. My brother was in the Corps.'

Tommy continues to demonstrate an unwillingness to acknowledge the family ISA, but instead alludes to further trauma experienced when serving in the marines. They then discuss their fractured relationship with Paddy.

Brendan, assertively, *'That has nothing to do with forgiveness. I got children. I got a family to protect. Everything I do is for them. I forgave Pop. Just like I forgave you and Mom.*

'You forgave us?...'[If] you leave you get to bury people.'

Brendan, candidly, *'You're not the only one who has suffered Tommy. I didn't even know she was sick. I didn't even get the chance to say goodbye to my own mother. You had no right to keep that from me, that was not your decision to make.'*

The scene ends with no resolution, they square up, stare each other down still full of resentment and fury before Tommy eventually turns his back and walks away. Joel Edgerton beautifully renders Brendan's frustration, allowing the attempted sincerity of his final speech to fall somewhat short. Tommy cannot be reasoned with, and the failure of Brendan's speech allows for the sympathy for both characters to remain absolutely even.

As the film progresses we find out that Tommy walked away from the Marines after his 'brother' was killed in a friendly fire accident. The RSA let him down; it was supposed to provide him with a sense of belonging and utility; an investment in the system; to allow ideological recognition.

However, his engagement with the Marines RSA ceases with him preforming a humane act when he rescues a group of Marines stuck in a submerged tank: Tommy demonstrates an innate morality beyond ideology. Tommy then further demonstrates his rejection of the family ISA, reacting with anger and cynicism when his father attempts to convey admiration for his heroics on the battlefield: *'Spare the compassionate father routine Pap.'*

Tommy won't submit to the rules: he has no walk-in music before each fight and walks straight out of the cage after he has knocked out his opponent; he constantly wears an expression of seething rage that is very difficult to not find exciting. Tommy's character exists in a state of ideological flux; one must have a place within the system. This is why Tommy cannot win, for him to do so would be to suggest that one can escape, redefine or even, simply, question the system. Instead he must be made to yield. And Brendan is the perfect subject to do so; a character whose life so perfectly involves all the *primary* Ideological State Apparatus. Brendan shows respect and manages to include further ISA in his walk out as he uses classical music- *Ode to joy-* to suggest a philosophy behind his fighting style, a logic. Brendan, as this perfectly interpellated figure, has to win, has to make Tommy capitulate.

Emma couldn't see this.

******

'Primary colours.' I suggested, trying to explain my love of the film.

She nods along, half sarcastically, 'Oh right, primary colours, I get that.'

I was looking forward to showing her *Warrior,* a throw-away filum in which I had found some value. The first time I showed her was after we had finished an afternoon encounter. I was still trying to convince her I didn't need a television so we lay in bed watching it on an iPad. The sound was shite, far too low. Everything lacked impact. We managed twenty minutes before resuming the afternoon encounter I had thought was by. So it was shelved and I forgot to ask her what she thought.

Six months later we were making suggestions about what to watch of an evening, 'Why don't we try that film you love so much?' I sensed condescension but she'd be won over once we got rolling. She settled on the couch, I set it up and laid down next to her.

'No, no, no. Not from the start.'

Perplexed, I shuffled around to her, 'What are

you talkin' about?'

'Don't play it from the start, I saw the first twenty minutes.'

'Aye, six months ago. Ye cannie do that, gotta see it as the director intended.' Not unreasonable to ask someone to watch a filum in its entirety after a six month gap.

She stifles a laugh, 'I remember what happened.' then looks at me and affects a soothing tone, 'Honestly, I can remember: brothers, fightin' an' that.' She smiles, sarcastically, but manages to keep the laughter down.

I'm surprised. A quiet anger builds, you'd think I would've found it funny, or I'd've been disappointed or nonplussed. But no. 'You don't want to watch it.'

'I'm not watching it if I have to sit through that again, it was interminable.'

'Why suggest watching it at all then?'

'Because I know you love it. And because I know you are writing about it.'

I ejected the DVD.

'What are you doing? Are you a fuckin' child?'

Hands up feigning ignorance, 'What? You don't want to watch it.'

'Jesus. Do this and I'm going home.'

I eventually concede and we start from the twenty minute mark. I can feel it immediately, she's no' havin' it.

Our man Tommy offers Mad Dog a scrap and Emma nails a joke, she is able to precis her entire argument in one little remark. As Tommy utters, *'I'll fight him.'*

Emma sits up, feigning interest, 'Here,' having gained my attention, her tone suggesting she is investing, she delivers, 'do you think he's going to win?' and rolls across me, laughing. An absolute nailer, note-perfect sarcasm. Fair play to her, she is right, I can't deny that it is easy to swipe the legs out from it.

I look at her, almost pleading, 'Uch, it's…you know…' she leans toward me opening her eyes wide anticipating my justification, '…primary colours.'

With a condescending nod, 'Ah, ok.' The nod turns to a head shake and smirk. Fuckin' torture.

I've never cared about the clichés before; if things are done well then you can forgive. I never get fed up of watching Tommy giving Mad Dog a proper bleachin': it's shot well, the camera bouncing with the canvas, struggling to keep pace with the fighters, with them out of shot at times or out of focus whilst we see the looks of shock and horror on the faces of the gathered crowd; the sound of Tommy's breathing and each landed blow helps provoke a physical reaction to the scene. I love it.

She sighs at the next scene when the gym owner and agent, Colt Boyd, approaches Paddy to find out more about Tommy.

'He put a beatin' on the number one middleweight contender in the world today. I want to know more about the guy…'

'Dae ye, aye?' she quips.

The sneering. I'm being judged, I've cowped off the tightrope with this one. A dud. And now I have to watch it with her commentary. I can feel her beautiful eyes judging me directly behind my head.

She struggles through Brendan's first fight after

incorrectly suggesting he'd lose. The trouper manages to tolerate the café scene between Paddy and Tommy anol. I like that scene.

We get as far as the jump to Marines stationed in Iraq and she loses it, 'Oh, what the fuck is this now? What's going on?' She follows the dialogue and then bursts into laughter when she sees the two images of Tommy which have supposedly sparked recognition in a young marine. She is right, for some reason they've made a cunt of this little note. She continues through laughter, 'Why is no one saying, *'Nah...you sure? That's no' him.'* and another fella agreeing with him, *'Aye, yer talkin' shite there mate.'* are you even sure that's him?'

I concede, 'Yeah, that is a bit odd.'

'I'm sorry Mark but I can't take much more of this.'

'Aye, I can sense that.' Fuck, it's not all like this, there are a couple crackin' scenes by anyone's standard. I keep a lid on it and whisper like a battered wean, head down, 'A lot of the second act is just scrappin' anyway,' almost pleading, 'can I show you Paddy's breakdown? And the ending?'

'Sure.' she smiles. What a terribly nice lady.

I skip the film forward a number of scenes and provide the context for the selected scenes. We watch the couple of minutes before Nick Nolte's big moment and Emma continues her dissection.

Laughing again, 'AWOL? You fuckin' kiddin' on? Cuz, oh aye, that's the best thing to do if you are hiding from the authorities, eh? Become an internet sensation and star in a nationally syndicated sports tournament! Many folk do you suppose would watch such a thing? Millions, eh?'

Sighing, 'Aye, millions.'

Laughing, 'Millions!'

I show her the interaction between Paddy and Tommy in the casino which leads to Paddy's breakdown: Tommy is unwilling to forgive his father and only restates his resentment toward him.

'*...I don't need you now. It's too late now...the only thing I have in common with Brendan Conlon is that we have absolutely no use for you...Yeah I was right. I think I liked you better when you were a drunk...Take it somewhere else, old man...Go back to the room and listen to some more fish stories no one gives a shit about. Go on, get outta here. Get the fuck outta here!*'

Emma didn't sarcastically, 'Ooft.' the casino scene, suggesting she thought it was well executed- a phrase which I would suggest is too clinical but would still attribute to her. She took in Paddy's scene quietly.

Paddy pished, stoats about his hotel room quoting Moby Dick before standing eye-to-eye with Tommy, screaming in his face. Tommy recognises the Paddy he remembers and, saying nothing, takes a sobbing Paddy in his arms before settling down on the hotel bed cuddling his dad, who has now spent his drunken aggression.

'*We're lost. We're all lost, Tommy. We'll never make it back.*'

I look at Emma who thinks briefly, then adjudges, 'Good scene.' There ye are. It was so. It was decreed a good scene by the grand arbiter; I apologise it was such a pitiful offering.

'Right, skip on: the finale.'

'Sure.' I skip.

'So who wins?'

'Guess.' Even as a big quiz fan, Emma rolled her eyes, disinterested in participating in this prediction task. Eventually she gave it a go.

'Tommy but he is underhanded so gets disqualified.'

Still skipping, 'Nup.'

Without hesitation, 'They won't finish the fight, exit as a draw.'

Now paused, 'Nup, guess again.'

'Brendan because Tommy won't land the killer blow.'

'Nup, guess again.'

'D'know what? I don't care.' Fair enough.

The scene plays out, she covers her eyes as blows are landed. I encourage her to actually watch the scene before attempting to ignore her in order to find enough space to enjoy the warm tears. Tommy pummels; Brendan takes his pummelling. Emma squirms and shakes her head as Brendan is smashed against the canvas- it's a response I suppose. The pupils from Brendan's school cheer him; Tess cheers him; his coach cheers him; all the time Tommy becomes more isolated.

In round three Brendan manages to get Tommy in a hold.

'Oh no, what's he doing?' She squirms, 'Oh no, no, no.' She covers her eyes not realising that it's her ears that need guarded. I smile and watch Emma's face as the loud *crack* of Tommy's shoulder breaking is heard.

'Fu-u-u-u-ck!'

Laughing, 'Sore yin, eh?'

'How could you let me watch that!? You know breaking bones is my one phobia!' I didn't know this- and it's one of a large number of single phobias.

'Shh, shh, shh. Watch it. Listen.'

Tommy fights on with the one arm and Brendan tries to reason with him. Emma settles back into it. I raise a finger as About Today swells and I start to feel the tears. The dropped hands, the faked move, the kick, the hold, the lines.

'I love you, I love you Tommy.'

She manages not to laugh, she can see I'm enjoying it. But as soon as the moment passes and the credits roll, 'I'm sorry but that was pure shite.'

Resignedly, 'It's not that bad.'

'Oh, it is.'

Turning to her, 'I told you, it's a filum I love. I never said it was a classic, you can enjoy filums without them being critically acclaimed. You can deviate, you are allowed to…to…disagree.'

She senses she has touched a nerve. Calmly, soothingly, with love, 'Ok.' She smiles at me until I slow down and smile back, 'Right, mon we'll watch Blade Runner.'

Do I still love this filum? It's not an immediate bang-on-the-table 'Yes!'; I, unfortunately, invest a lot in what she thinks.

Every word I now type seems silly: *she was right*. The dialogue, the mythical names, the premise. The very idea that it could be dissected seriously. Each scene, each line, each little note, undermined. And I'm not even talking about the faults which are obvious at first reading and cannot be reconciled: Brendan's question to his wife, 'Where is the rest of that skirt?'; the gratuitous arse shot of Jennifer Morrison as she squats down in her pants next to Brendan; and it's failure of the Bechdel test on two counts. Little theme there.

I've tried to watch it since, tried to *go along* as I did before. All its laziness and flaws are now more obvious but I still love it, I still see what I saw before.

Funny though, it has never been in my top five films:

Moon

Blade Runner

Senna

Consequences of Love

Mean Streets

ABOUT THE AUTHOR

R.G Robertson is a novelist and playwright from Scotland.

Made in the USA
Lexington, KY
14 May 2018